Pra

MW00653399

"The big ideas in this small book is insanely genius. It is a terrific resource for anyone interested in living sane in an insane world. This book distinguishes itself by not only talking about real issues, but working through them. The hypothesis of mental health is a tough nut to crack, but Ms. Jackson cracked it wide open."

-Arleana Waller, ShePower Ambassador, Leadership Consultant, Professional Speaker, Author of *369 Things a Woman Must Enjoy Before She Dies*

"This book is not only timely, but extremely relevant as the world we live in begins to feel less and less predictable by the day. The text provides great examples and is easily digestible for a wide range of audiences. I believe many people will be able to better optimize their mental health with the help of this book."

-Joy Harden Bradford, Licensed Psychologist, Creator of *Therapy for Black Girls*, Featured in O, The Oprah Magazine, Atlanta, GA

"Staying Sane in an Insane World helps us to see mental health for what it is, a normal part of everyone's life, that should be managed just like our physical health. In this book, Ms. Jackson shares vivid stories and examples to inspire us to make mental health a daily priority."

-Dr. George James, LMFT, Therapist, Speaker, Consultant, Relationship & Mental Health Expert, Media Personality, CEO of George Talks, LLC, Co- Author of *The C.A.L.L: Inspiring Stories for Young Men about Character, Accountability, Love & Leadership,* Philadelphia, PA

Staying SANE

IN AN INSANE WORLD:

A Prescription for Even Better Mental Health

Kiaundra Jackson, LMFT

To stay connected and receive updates, please
visit:

www.stayingsaneworld.com

Dedication

This book is dedicated to all my family members and close friends. You can do anything you put your mind to if you believe! I lovingly dare you to pursue your dreams, defy the odds, and live within your passion.

"The definition of insanity is doing the same thing over and over again and expecting a different result."

—Albert Einstein

Contents

Author's Note

L ife is a journey full of ups, downs, twists, and uncertainties. We live in a "microwave" society where it seems like everything needs to be done *now*. Our family members, spouses, and children need us. We have to work, cook, clean, and take care of our basic necessities. Do not even get me started on the endless emails, text messages, and social media notifications that compete for our attention. The daily demands of life, also known as stressors, take a toll on us – not only physically, but mentally.

If we are not careful, stressors can overwhelm us to the point where our mental health is at risk. As you go through your days, I urge you to ask yourself, "What is my process for managing stress? How do I handle unexpected circumstances? Is the way I feel right now healthy or harmful?"

Through this book, I hope that I encourage you to pay attention to your thoughts, feelings, and emotions, and learn to spot the warning signs of mental health issues. I do not want you to go through life pretending like problems do not exist, but I want to help you navigate through life and provide you with the tools necessary for optimal mental health and overall well-being.

…Let's get started!

Introduction

Mental health is one of those concepts that often goes ignored. Because mental health is intangible, it is often placed in a different category than other illnesses. We have to realize that mental health issues should be taken as seriously as any physical ailments or difficult circumstance that we deal with in life. Just because you do not see it, does not mean it does not exist.

We need to pay attention to our mental health just like we do our physical health. Mental illness is just as real as a cyst, mass, or other dysfunctions. Just like you should exercise regularly and make wise food choices to keep your physical body in shape, you should take the time and effort to maintain an omal level of mental health.

You may not realize it, but the state of your mental health impacts both you and those around you. It can greatly alter your mood, affect your work performance, or hinder your ability to complete a task. No one on this planet today can afford to ignore their mental health. It is important to make intentional wellness choices daily so that we can stay sane.

How are you staying sane?

Chapter 1
Mental Health 101

"Not until we are lost do we begin to understand ourselves."

—Henry David Thoreau

DID YOU KNOW?

Only approximately 17% of adults in the U.S. operate in a state of optimal mental health.

O ne of my personal and professional missions is to help people understand that our mental health should be treated just like we treat our physical health. Since mental struggles are often not expressed externally, we tend to think it does not exist. Too often, we ignore behaviors and triggers that can result in negative consequences in our lives and relationships.

At its basic level, mental health includes our emotional, psychological, and social well-being. It affects how we think, feel, and act. It also helps determine how we handle stress, relate to others, and make choices. Mental health is important at every stage of life, from childhood and adolescence to adulthood.

Remember when you were a child and the only real worry that you had in life was going to school, making and keeping friends, and writing love letters to your crush during class? *Do you like me? Yes, no, maybe... check the box.* Those were the days, right?

In your early years, riding your bike, playing hopscotch outside, skating, getting dirty, and being in the house before the street lights came on were the only real concerns you had. Then, you grew up and became a teenager with more responsibilities. You had to balance school, chores, and perhaps a part-time job. The boy or girl who used to get on your nerves suddenly attracted your attention; maybe you even started dating. You gave an eye-roll each time you heard the word "curfew."

Still, nothing could prepare you for the realities of adulthood. When adulthood came, it hit you hard. You were excited about your first paycheck, until you realized that most of it went to taxes, your monthly rent, utilities, and transportation expenses – not to mention food, clothing, basic necessities, and the all-time favorite – student loan payments. Add a spouse and children in the mix, and "adulting" became even more complex.

Do you see what I mean when I say that your mental health is important at each stage of life? In fact, your mental state often becomes more fragile as you progress through life. As an adult, you have experienced so much of life's ups and downs that you might wish to go back to your younger days when it seemed life was so much simpler.

Now, let's be real. What I mentioned about the bliss of your childhood is not 100% applicable for everyone. There are difficult circumstances that can occur at any age – deaths, relationship strains, financial troubles, medical issues, and bullying are just a few examples. Take a moment to think about how you handled difficult times.

I like to use the example of a vending machine when discussing mental health with others. When we make a purchase from a vending machine, we usually put in our money, make a selection and receive exactly what we were craving at that moment. There is a direct exchange of money for snacks. Sometimes, however, the vending machine malfunctions and our scrumptious treat gets stuck. What do we do?

Typically, we immediately move into problem solving mode. We might put in more money to see if the first snack will drop along with a new one. If that plan is unsuccessful, we might bang on the glass, hoping that any movement will help the snack get "unstuck." When all else fails, we resort to no longer just simply hitting the glass, but moving the entire machine. As the frustration builds, we put our entire weight on the vending machine, becoming the Incredible Hulk just to get a snack, that most likely, was not even a healthy choice for our bodies.

Now, you are probably thinking – how does a vending machine relate to mental health? Just as a vending machine can deliver an unexpected result, life is guaranteed to bring us unpleasant surprises. When an unforeseen circumstance comes, what is your first coping strategy? How do you respond when you are faced with something difficult?

What you do, how you do it, where you do it, the choices you make, and the people you involve in the process are all a part of your mental health. The goal is always upward and onward. Before I recommend tools you can use to achieve and maintain your mental health, we have to be able to identify our own responses to life when our "snack gets stuck in the vending machine."

What was a "vending machine" moment in your life?

Kiaundra Jackson, LMFT

Notes:

_____

_____

_____

_____

_____

STAYING SANE
VIDEO BREAK #1

GO HERE TO WATCH THIS FREE VIDEO:

WWW.STAYINGSANEWORLD.COM/CH1

Chapter 2
Knowing When Something is Wrong: How to Identify Symptoms

"Admitting that you need help…doesn't make you broke. It makes you fixable. And teachable."

—Unknown

The more you admit your weaknesses, the sooner the healing process can begin. Alcoholics Anonymous is known for its 12-step recovery program, which can be applied to any area of your life where you need to experience healing. One of the most impactful first steps in Alcoholics Anonymous is admittance. Being honest enough to make a bold declaration of your need is a must. Now, I am not telling you to go air your dirty laundry to a room full of strangers. But it is important to find at least one other person in your life whom you can trust to share your areas of struggle.

Confession is powerful!

How can you fix a problem if you do not even know it exists? How can you fix something that you are unwilling to address? It is easy to take pride in our refusal to acknowledge our pain. However, it is not healthy to continuously dismiss situations that have produced hurt, anger, regret, fear, or other negative emotions in us. Be courageous enough to stand in the mirror, look at yourself and say "I am not okay. I am struggling right now. I am not at my best. I need some help."

Sometimes it is tough to avoid feeling stress from pressures that can build up in life. There are two major types of stressors: situational and biological.

- Situational: Death, loss of relationships, life transitions (having a baby, divorce, starting a new job, moving, going to college, etc.)

- Biological: Predispositions to mental illness or mental health issues that run in your family

Worrying about these stressors periodically is normal, but if you come to the point where your worry negatively impacts certain areas of your life, you should seek help. If you experience any of the following, you may have deeper issues that you need to explore:

- Often feel extreme anger or worry
- Sleep too much or too little
- Engage in reckless behaviors that can harm you or others
- Relationship difficulties (family, friends, colleagues, peers)
- Feeling extensive grief for longer than 6 months after a loss or death
- Belief that your mind is controlled or out of control
- Use of alcohol or drugs
- Eating too much or too little
- Isolation from others
- Frequent or uncontrollable bouts of crying
- No desire to go to work or school

- Changes in sex drive or libido

- Disengagement from formerly pleasurable activities or hobbies

Take a moment to ponder and write down any areas in your life that you need to examine. Can you identify with any symptoms on the list?

Notes:

_____

_____

_____

_____

_____

DID YOU KNOW?

Mental illness does not respect any boundaries of race, ethnicity, class, geographical location, sexual orientation, religious preferences, or socioeconomic status.

If you have experienced even one symptom from the above list for two weeks or more, it is time to speak to a professional. There is nothing to be ashamed of if you need to visit a therapist. Remember, the first step to recovery is being honest with yourself enough to seek help when it is needed. There are people who have an amazing passion and heart to help people through the roughest times in their lives. Seeking help is a strength, not a weakness. The strongest people stay that way because they are not afraid to ask for help; they are willing to admit when something is wrong.

No one is exempt from life's struggles, even the ones that we think have a perfect life and have it all together. There have been countless stories in the media where the celebrities that many of us admire have had their own battles with mental health. I am sure there are some celebrities on this list that you had no clue struggled with mental health issues at some point in their life.

1. Alicia Keys: Depression

2. Serena Williams: Depression

3. DMX: Substance Use and Bipolar Disorder

4. Drew Carey: Depression

5. Catherine Zeta-Jones: Bipolar II Disorder

6. Brooke Shields: Post-Partum Depression

7. Elton John: Substance Use and Bulimia

8. Paula Deen: Panic Disorder and Agoraphobia

9. Brittney Spears: Depression and Bipolar Disorder

10. Jim Carey: Depression

11. Michael Phelps: Attention Deficit Hyperactivity Disorder (ADHD)

12. Demi Lovato: Bulimia

13. Katie Perry: Depression

14. Halle Berry: Depression

15. Mel Gibson: Depression

16. Ashley Judd: Depression

17. Brandon Marshall: Borderline Personality Disorder

18. Jenifer Lewis: Bipolar Disorder

19. Chris Brown: Bipolar Disorder and Post-Traumatic Stress Disorder (PTSD)

20. Jesse Jackson, Jr: Bipolar II Disorder

Did any of the names on this list surprise you? Does knowing their struggle with mental illness make you think differently about them? Why or why not?

Notes:

_____

_____

_____

_____

_____

STAYING SANE

VIDEO BREAK #2

GO HERE TO WATCH THIS FREE VIDEO:

WWW.STAYINGSANEWORLD.COM/CH2

Chapter 3
Ways to Manage Life:
50 Positive Coping Skills

"Peace is not the absence of conflict, but the ability to cope with it."

—Dorothy Thomas

DID YOU KNOW?
1 in 4 people have experienced a
mental health issue within the past 12 months.

W e all can agree that certain periods in our life can be extremely difficult. At times, life throws us obstacles that are simply unavoidable. Everyone experiences hardships, difficulties, failures, losses, and setbacks that impact their lives. However, it is important that we develop a healthy perspective from which to view life's challenges. Strong mental health is built and sustained by how we deal with our daily stressors.

Each person handles stress differently; over time, we rely on strategies that feel normal and safe. However, it is important to step back and evaluate how these strategies impact our lives and those around us. Our response to life's stressors reveals the type of coping strategies we have developed, whether positive or negative. If you exercise or take quiet time alone to process your emotions, for instance, those are positive coping strategies. If you resort to overeating or drug and alcohol use to avoid reality, those are negative coping strategies.

You probably can think of someone you know who dealt with stress in an unhealthy manner and suffered as a result. Negative coping strategies put pressure on your relationships. They can damage your body or create long-term emotional pain, even when they seem helpful initially. In extreme cases, negative coping strategies can ruin lives.

To decide whether a coping strategy is positive or negative, it is helpful to analyze the short and long-term impact of your behavior on yourself and others. Negative coping strategies are typically quick fixes that will have adverse long-term impact. Positive coping strategies sometimes require more investment of time and energy than the negative strategies, but engaging in these activities can boost your mental health in major ways.

Below is a list of 50 positive coping skills you can engage in today:

1. Take deep breaths

2. Engage in an enjoyable activity

3. Play sports

4. Think of something funny

5. Meditate

6. Use a stress ball

7. Dance

8. Write a letter to yourself, friend or family member

9. Take a quick walk

10. Stand up and stretch

11. Read a magazine

12. Count to 100

13. Cook/bake

14. Use positive affirmations (Ex: I am beautiful)

15. Identify your emotions

16. Express your feelings to someone

17. Identify a positive thought

18. Play a card game

19. Organize something

20. Listen to music

21. Talk to a friend

22. Take a time out

23. Look at pictures you have taken

24. Watch a good movie

25. Write a list of positive qualities about yourself

26. Garden

27. Take pictures

28. Use positive self-talk

29. Make a list for the future

30. Compliment yourself

31. Smile at others

32. Read inspirational quotes

33. Write down your thoughts

34. List 10 positive things about yourself

35. Tell someone you are thankful for them

36. Listen to nature sounds

37. Sit and relax all your muscles

38. Watch a funny video

39. Use a relaxation app

40. Notice five beautiful things in your

environment

41. Laugh

42. Smile in the mirror

43. Hug a stuffed animal

44. Paint

45. Pop bubble wrap

46. Sing

47. Give someone a hug

48. Exercise

49. Play a game

50. Say, "I can do this!"

The next time you are tempted to engage in a negative coping strategy for temporary relief, pick from this list instead. What I love most about this list is that it does not cost money to engage in any of these activities; you can use any of them at any time.

Write down ten positive coping skills that
you want to incorporate the next time you are
faced with a stressful situation.

Notes:

_____

_____

_____

_____

_____

STAYING SANE
VIDEO BREAK #3

Go Here To Watch This Free Video:
WWW.STAYINGSANEWORLD.COM/CH3

Chapter 4
Mental Health
vs.
Mental Illness

"Those who suffer from mental illness are stronger than you think. We must fight to go to work, care for our families, be there for our friends, and act 'normal' while battling unimaginable pain."

—Unknown

Mental health and mental illness are often used interchangeably in our society. However, there is a distinct difference that needs to be noticed and recognized so we no longer confuse the two. Mental illness is serious and it causes major impairments in one's life. It is not something that you would even wish upon your worst enemy.

Mental health is a state of optimal well-being in which people are able to cope with the stressors of life, work productively, and able to make contributions to their community. *Mental illness* occurs when parts of your brain do not function properly. Consequently, there is perpetual disruption to your mental state and how you feel, think, communicate and behave.

When the brain does not function properly, there are typically 6 functions that can be distorted:

- Thinking

- Perception

- Emotions

- Signaling

- Physical

- Behaviors

Symptoms of mental illness can include a variety of physiological, emotional, and psychological changes (see list on page 12-13). When these symptoms cause significant impairments in your daily life, it is often a sign of mental illness. Mental illness can bring a distinct set of challenges, but they can be managed. Most individuals who struggle with mild to moderate mental illness can function well with the help of family members, friends, medication (if needed), and continuous therapy.

In today's information age, Google has become our best friend; it seems that everything we need to know can be found through a swipe or a few keyboard strokes. The internet is a great place to gather information, but it can be dangerous if you attempt to research medical and mental health diagnoses. Please do not attempt to diagnose yourself.

While it is good to be informed, it is probably one of the worst things you can do when it comes to mental health issues because you run the risk of misdiagnosing yourself and receiving incorrect information. In all honesty, self-diagnosis can be harmful because it can keep you from getting the help you actually need. If you start to feel strange or notice that you are experiencing symptoms of mental illness, you should always speak with your primary care physician or mental health professional, as they will have greater expertise on your specific situation. In the final section of this book, I will list the different types of mental health professionals so that you can determine the one most suitable for you.

Mental Health vs. Mental Illness

Mental Health
- *Adequate Self-Concept**
- *Positive Coping Skills*
- *Good Problem Solving & Decision-Making Skills*
- *Independent*
- *Reality-based thinking*
- *Sets goals*
- *Optimistic*
- *Able to comprehend delayed gratification*
- *Effective socialization*

Mental Illness
- *Poor Self-Concept**
- *Negative Coping Skills*
- *Poor Problem Solving & Decision-Making Skills*
- *Dependent*
- *Distorted thinking patterns*
- *Poor goal setting*
- *Pessimistic*
- *Need for immediate gratification*
- *Extreme isolation*

*Self-Concept: An idea of the self that is constructed from the beliefs one hold about oneself and the responses of others.

Now that you understand the difference between mental health and mental illness, it is important that you understand how to achieve and maintain a healthy mental state. I mentioned previously in Chapter 2 that there are some situational and biological predispositions that are unavoidable. If you see any symptoms of mental illness in your life, the positive coping strategies from Chapter 3 can start you on the path to healing.

Notes:

_____

_____

_____

_____

_____

STAYING SANE

VIDEO BREAK #4

GO HERE TO WATCH THIS FREE VIDEO:

WWW.STAYINGSANEWORLD.COM/CH4

Conclusion
Your Final Prescription
and
Mental Health Checklist

"Health is the state of complete physical, mental and social well-being, and not merely the absence of disease or infirmities."

—World Health Organization

We are living in a world where there are so many external factors that affect our daily lives. In my own private practice, I have seen an increase in depression and anxiety in many people. If you find that you are need of mental health services, do not feel ashamed or embarrassed – value yourself enough to get help. To stay sane in an insane world, here is your final prescription:

Name: *You*

Address: _____ Date: *Today*

Final Prescription

- Treat your mental health with the same importance as your physical health.

- Take note of major changes in your thoughts, feelings, emotions, and behaviors.

- Do not try to diagnose yourself – if you consistently experience symptoms of mental health issues for longer than 2 weeks, promptly schedule an appointment with your doctor or mental health professional.

- Practice positive coping skills daily.

- Never give up on yourself.

REFILL *as needed*

Kiaundra Jackson

SIGNATURE

STAYING SANE
MENTAL HEALTH CHECKLIST

Go Here To Get This Free PDF Download:
WWW.STAYINGSANEWORLD.COM/PDF

EPILOGUE

Now that you have some basic tools to help you achieve an optimal state of mental health, I want to provide you with knowledge of how to obtain mental health services. Once you have made the bold decision to seek help, it is important for you to know the coverage options that are available to you. Three of the most common options are below:

1. **EAP (Employee Assistance Program):** A program through which some companies offer to pay for employees' short-term counseling sessions (normally 3 to 6 sessions). Companies who provide this service typically provide you with a list of mental health professionals in your area that you can use. You pay

nothing unless you choose to attend more than the allotted amount of sessions.

2. **Health Insurance Companies**: Most health insurance companies offer mental health services within their network. Similar to EAP, health insurance companies will provide you with a list of mental health professionals locally that are within their network. In most cases, if you choose to go with a provider on this list, all you need to do is pay your co-payment at the time of your counseling sessions. The mental health professional will bill your health insurance for the difference.

3. **Paying out of your own pocket**: If you do not have access to EAP or health insurance, or prefer not to be limited to a particular list when choosing a mental health professional, you can always opt to pay the full rate for services.

TIPS:

- Contact your employer's human resources department to see if they offer any employer assistance services.

- Contact your health insurance provider or check their website to see if mental health services are available through your health insurance plan.

- One of my favorite websites I refer people to is www.psychologytoday. com. It is an online database where you can search therapists by geographical location, fees, specialties, ethnicities, and so much more. It is a one-stop shop to finding a therapist that fits your needs.

Choosing a Therapist

1. Most therapists offer a phone consultation to get to know more about your needs, discuss fees, and to make sure they can help you. On this

call, ask all the questions you need to make sure you feel comfortable and understand the process.

Questions to consider asking: Do you take my insurance? What are your specialties? Where are you located? What are your office hours? Do you have experience working with others who have the same issues I currently have?

TIP: It is okay to call and have phone consultations with more than one therapist until you find the one who seems to relate to you most. This phone consultation process is similar to an interview. You are interviewing to see if they are a good fit for you also and that they understand your needs.

2. Once you select a therapist, you can begin the intake process with that person. An intake appointment is where you go to the office, fill

out paperwork with your contact information, and discuss past and present issues/symptoms. This appointment allows the therapist to understand your history and background, and determine how they can best help you.

TIP: During your first meeting with a therapist, you are getting to know them as much as they are getting to know you. You want to make sure this is a person with whom you will feel comfortable sharing intimate details of your life. They should be objective, understanding and non-judgmental.

3. When you find a good therapist, stick with that person and attend all of your scheduled counseling sessions, even when you start to feel better. When your sessions are over, keep that therapists' information just in case you need to schedule future visits.

Types of Mental Health Professionals

The primary goal for all mental health professionals is to help you to understand and cope with your thoughts, feelings and behaviors. They provide guidance that helps you develop better ways of thinking and living, cultivate life skills, and improve your relationships. Mental health professionals may also help you assess and diagnosis mental illness.

Selecting the right mental health professional can seem overwhelming at first. If you understand the various roles and specialties that are in the mental health field, it makes the process easier. To help you with your search, I have included categories of mental health professionals and their basic description in the list below. This list is not exhaustive, but it gives you a starting point for the most common mental health needs.

Primary Care Physicians

Primary care physicians (PCP) and pediatricians

can prescribe medication, but do not specialize in mental health care. It is best that you work with both your primary care physician and a mental health professional to determine the best treatment plan. As more mental health issues arise in society, more primary care physicians are being trained and equipped to provide mental health care.

Psychiatrists

Psychiatrists are licensed medical doctors with medical and psychiatric training. They can diagnose mental health conditions and prescribe and monitor medications. Psychiatrists are also able to offer counseling and provide therapy. Some have special training in child and adolescent mental health or substance use disorders or geriatric psychiatry.

Clinical Social Workers

Clinical social workers have a master's degree in social work and are trained to make diagnoses and provide individual and group counseling, case management and advocacy. Clinical social workers often work in hospitals, clinics, or in private practice.

Marriage and Family Therapists

Marriage and family therapists are mental health practitioners trained in psychotherapy and family systems. They are licensed within one or more states to diagnose and treat emotional and mental disorders in couples and families; they also help improve relationship dynamics.

Licensed Professional Clinical Counselors

Licensed professional clinical counselors are master's-degreed mental health service providers, trained to work with individuals, families, and groups in treating mental, behavioral, and emotional problems and disorders.

Clinical Psychologists

Clinical psychologists with a doctoral degree in psychology (such as a Ph.D. or Psy.D.)

are trained to make diagnoses and provide individual and group therapy. Some may have training in specific forms of therapy like cognitive behavioral therapy, along with other behavioral therapy interventions.

School Psychologists

School psychologists with advanced degrees in psychology are trained to make diagnoses, and provide individual and group therapy. They also work with parents, teachers and school staff to ensure a healthy school environment. They may participate in the development of individualized education plans (IEP) to help improve the school experience of the student with a mental health condition.

Pastoral Counselors

Pastoral counselors and chaplains are clergy members with training in clinical pastoral education. They are trained to diagnose and provide counseling, and can receive certification equivalent to a doctorate in counseling.

Additional Helpful Information:

- Weigh out all options before committing to one therapist

- Do not be afraid to ask questions

- Ask about the therapist's education/ theoretical approach/ style of counseling

- It is okay to call multiple therapists for phone consultations and attend multiple intake appointments until you find the best person

- Phone consultations are free, most intake sessions are not free

- Be specific about your goals and what you want to accomplish in counseling

- Therapists are not magicians – they cannot wave a magic wand and make all your issues disappear. It takes effort and time to achieve and sustain optimal mental health.

- Attend your scheduled sessions regularly

- Seek help from a therapist you trust and connect with

- Always be open and honest (the therapist cannot help you if you are not being truthful)

- Individual sessions are typically 50 minutes

- Sessions for couples and families are typically 90 minutes

- Most sessions are weekly (as you make progress, the frequency of session may decrease to bi-weekly, once per month etc.)

Notes

Author's Note

1.   McGue, Matt, and Thomas J. Bouchard, Jr.
"Genetic and Environmental Influences on
Human Behavioral Differences." *Annual
Review of Neuroscience. Volume* 21 (1998):
1-24.

Chapter 1: Mental Health 101

1.   "Mental Health by the Numbers." NAMI:
National Alliance on Mental Illness. https://
www.nami.org/Learn-More/Mental-Health-
By-the-Numbers.

2.   "What Is Mental Health?" MentalHealth.
Gov https://www.mentalhealth.gov/basics/
what-is-mental-health/index.html

Chapter 2: Knowing When Something is Wrong: How to Identify Symptoms

1. "29 Celebrities Who Overcame Mental Illness and Depression." Morningside Recovery. https://www.morningsiderecovery.com/blog/29-celebrities-that-overcame-mental-illness/

2. "50 Famous Celebrities That Suffer From Mental Disorders." Lifestyle Passion. http://www.lifestylepassion.com/25-1/50-famous-celebrities-that-suffer-from-mental-disorders/

3. "Facts about Specific Diagnoses." Mental Health Reporting. University of Washington School of Social Work. http://depts.washington.edu/mhreport/facts_diagnoses.php

4. "Mental Health: Culture, Race, and Ethnicity: A Supplement to Mental Health: A Report of the Surgeon General." U.S. Department of Health and Human Services [DHHS], 1999 https://www.ncbi.nlm.nih.gov/books/NBK44246/

Chapter 3: Ways to Manage Life: 50 Positive Coping Skills

1. "Coping Skills in Times of Stress." Mindful Occupation. http://mindfuloccupation.org/coping-skills-in-times-of-stress/

Chapter 4: Mental Health vs. Mental Illness

1. "Mental Health Basics." Centers for Disease Control and Prevention. 2013 https://www.cdc.gov/mentalhealth/basics.htm

2. "Understanding Mental Health and Mental Illness." TeenMentalHealth.org. https://www.slideshare.net/teenmentalhealth/understanding-mental-health-and-mental-illness-presentation

Epilogue

1. "Types of Mental Health Professionals." National Alliance on Mental Health (NAMI). https://www.nami.org/Learn-More/Treatment/Types-of-Mental-Health-Professionals

About the Author

Kiaundra Jackson is the visionary of KW Couples Therapy, and the Co-Founder of KW Essential Services and Black Speakers Rock. She has been featured in the Huffington Post as one of the "10 Black Female Therapists You Should Know." She is a trusted and Licensed Marriage and Family Therapist that gets results. As a graduate of Azusa Pacific University, she currently serves as private practitioner for individuals, couples and families. Her therapeutic approach is holistic, eclectic, and tailored to my client(s) needs to make sure each person is cared for biologically, emotionally, and spiritually.

In her early years as a therapist, Kiaundra developed a passion for helping couples deepen their intimacy, strengthen their relationships and uncover their true potential. Her vision is to help 10,000 couples heal their relationships, prevent divorce, and keep families together. Additional areas of expertise include: anger management, addiction, anxiety and depression, life transition, grief, loss and bereavement, and faith-based counseling.

Kiaundra provides support and practical feedback to help clients effectively address personal life challenges. She integrates complementary methodologies with compassion and understanding. She works with each individual, couple, or family to help build on their strengths and attain the personal growth they are committed to accomplishing.

CPSIA information can be obtained
at www.ICGtesting.com
Printed in the USA
BVHW082159280821
615076BV00005B/16